To Órlaith,

With love from Sinéad.

Aug 1st 1985.

THE
BUTTERFLY BALL
AND
THE GRASSHOPPER'S FEAST
ALAN ALDRIDGE

WITH VERSES BY
WILLIAM PLOMER

AND NATURE NOTES BY
RICHARD FITTER
REVISED BY EDWARD G. ATKINS
FOR AMERICAN EDITION

Grossman Publishers

A Division of The Viking Press
New York   1975

Based on William Roscoe's *The Butterfly Ball and the Grasshopper's Feast* (1807)
Design, Illustrations and Nature Notes Copyright © 1973 by
Aurelia Enterprises Ltd.
Verses © 1973 by William Plomer
Copyright © 1975 by The Viking Press, Inc.
All rights reserved
Published in 1975 by Grossman Publishers
625 Madison Avenue, New York, N.Y. 10022
Printed in U.S.A.

Library of Congress Cataloging in Publication Data
Aldridge, Alan.
    The butterfly ball and the grasshopper's feast.
    "Based on William Roscoe's The butterfly ball and the
grasshopper's feast (1807)."
    Summary: The gadfly, dormouse, mole, hare, and
other creatures prepare for the elegant, glittering
Butterfly Ball and Grasshopper Feast. Nature notes
on each animal are appended.
    [1. Stories in rhyme. 2. Animals—Fiction]
I. Plomer, William Charles Franklyn, 1903–
II. Fitter, Richard Sidney Richmond. III. Roscoe,
William, 1753–1831. The butterfly ball and the
grasshopper's feast. IV. Title.
PZ8.3.A366Bu4   [Fic]   75-19329
ISBN 0-670-19786-6

The twenty-eight colour plates by Alan Aldridge were prepared

in collaboration with Harry Willock

THIS IS THE DAY!

S NIGHT turns to dimness and draws back its curtain,
Stars, those bright sequins, now all disappear,
As dimness grows radiant, dawn makes it certain
That butterfly weather, quite perfect, is here;

Thundery cumulus masses are drifting
Very far off; overhead, very high,
Cirrus clouds spread their pink feathers, then lifting,
Dissolve and are lost in the turquoise-blue sky;

Up comes the Sun, and the very long shadows
Grow shorter; his light is like amber; the glow,
Where grey mists have melted away from the meadows,
Starts dewdrops all sparkling like jewels below;

Creatures that fly, or that creep, hop, or run,
Now wake all at once at a loud trumpet-call
To tell them this greatest of days has begun –
The day of the Feast and the Butterfly Ball!

At the sound of the trumpet the dozens invited
Now jump out of bed, squealing, "This is the day!
Oh, goody! The Ball! Aren't you madly excited?
Get up and get ready! Let's be on our way!"

TANTARA, teroo!
I'm Harold the Herald,
Gadfly and trumpeter too,
Well equipped for my job, as you see.
My trumpet's a gentian,
My sword's in its scabbard,
My wife, let me mention,
Embroidered my tabard
With stitches as fine as can be.

Tantara, teroo!
Wake up and take notice,
This news is important for you!
Today is a great day for all
In the insect creation
(And that is a rhyme for
Jollification),
So do be in time for
The magnificent Butterfly Ball!

PS.   *At dawn, when sunshine with a flood*
       Of light fills all the sky with gold,
       The Gadfly's wife (so I've been told)
       Besides the paper and the post
       Brings him a morning cup of blood,
       Not just because he likes it most;
       It is in fact his only food
       And puts him in a sanguine mood
       For doing almost anything,
       But most of all for trumpeting.

Plate 1

DORMOUSE is a sleepy mouse
But this is not a sleepy house,
        It's Honeysuckle Hall,
And Saffron Dormouse and her son
(His name is Tom) are full of fun,
        They're going to the Ball.

Yesterday she washed her hair
(All over) knowing she would wear
        Today her smartest thing,
Her picture hat heaped up with fruit;
Tom has put on his sailor suit
        And she her ruby ring.

Dormice in winter like to snooze,
Not now! Look at her party shoes,
        And oh, what lovely eyes!
Her husband married her because
He thought her finest feature was
        Their lustre and their size.

Plate 2

AMONG his home-made tunnels is the deep, dark hole,
The secret home and hide-out of Old Blind Mole,
And as he's not a tidy Mole
It's not a tidy hidey-hole.
It's dusty, musty, dingy, and on the floor he scatters
Half-chewed scraps of worms and things; he doesn't think it matters.

Now to him, deep underground,
Faintly there comes a thrilling sound —
Harold the Herald's trumpet call
Announcing that tonight's the Ball!

Up gets Mole to brush his sleeves
Free from earth and bits of leaves;
Meaning today to look his best
Before he went to bed he pressed
Under his mattress with much care
The velvet coat he means to wear.

He slips it on, puts on his hat,
Takes up his stick; as for his lunch,
He has no worry about that —
A bunch of juicy worms to munch.

 LONG the seashore near St Michael's Mount,
The sea quite calm beneath a mild blue sky,
On his high-stepping grey so proud and smart
Rich Dandy Rat, the merchant, canters by.

With satin saddle-cloth and silver spurs,
Silk, lace and feathers, feeling at his best,
Much looking forward to the Ball tonight,
To being admired because superbly dressed,

"How fine I am!" he thinks, "I only wish
The crew could see me from that ship becalmed."
All in a flash he finds himself attacked
By four fierce footpads, dangerously armed.

With pitchfork, cutlass, and goat-headed club
There's Oswald Otter, What's-his-name the Stoat,
Reynard DeAth the Fox, and Barney Bat —
They mean to rob him and then cut his throat.

They drag him down, they grab his cloak and sword,
Tear off his clothes, and find his heavy purse.
Out roll gold coins! While over these they fight
Dandy, like lightning, fearing something worse,

Darts through the bushes, racing for his life,
Not mounted now, nor dressed up for the Ball.
When he arrives there, somebody will squeak
"Disgraceful! Dandy Rat's got nothing on at all!"

PS. *Before you turn over, here's a good game —*
Hunt through the picture and find out Stoat's name.

(The answer is on the last page of the book)

Plate 4

ERE I come, here I come!
　　I'm Harlequin Hare!
I jingle and jangle, tinkle and strum!
I'm mad, and enjoy it! I make them all stare
Turning head-over-heels now and then in mid-air!

　　　　I'm ready and willing
　　　　To box for a shilling,
Can sprint like a flash, and play crazy new tricks;
　　　　If I get in a fix
　　　　What do I care?
　　　　I'm Harlequin Hare!

The madder the gladder's my motto, as all
　　　　Who see me agree;
I prance and I dance, and I caracole on
With cymbals and bells and accordion.
　　　　You can bet that I'll be
In good time tonight for the Butterfly Ball —
　　　　Harlequin Hare
Will be there, will be there!

Plate 5

ESMERALDA, Seraphina and Camilla
Each a glad and glorious Caterpillar,
A live mosaic of orange, green and gold,
What silks they wear! What gorgeous bags they hold!
But oh, they're slow! — yet safe if they're unseen
By any hungry crow, or other airborne wretch.

Creeping through grasses and the purple vetch
Almost as soundless as the bindweed twining
Among the flowers, with smiling sunlight shining
Through their enchanting parasols, with happy sighs
All three are whispering of that dream-come-true
When they'll be different beauties — Butterflies!

Belles of the Ball they hope to be ("Oh, do
Please introduce me to that lovely Caterpillar").
All Caterpillars have the hugest appetite,
So Esmeralda, Seraphina and Camilla
Can hardly wait to join the Feast tonight.

Plate 6

MAJOR Nathaniel Gnat
With his fine-feathered Cavalier hat
    Is off on a spree,
    So with you or with me
He cannot stop now for a chat.

He sleeps in a four-poster bed
With a canopy over his head,
    He lives in great state,
    He dines off gold plate,
And oh, what a life he has led!

On camels' and elephants' backs
In deserts and forests and shacks,
    In Tibet or Peru
    He has known what to do
In ambushes, raids and attacks.

The call to adventure he hears
Has made him shoot tigers and bears,
    And it quickens his pace
    When a beautiful face
Or an elegant figure appears.

Though asked to the Ball, I suppose
He may visit some lady he knows,
    Look deep in her eyes
    And bewitch her with lies
And present her, of course, with that rose.

Plate 7

HAPPY-Go-Lucky Grasshopper
Snatched up a gamp and clapped on a wig,
He doesn't care how he looks,
    Just doesn't care a fig!

For hours he's been hopping
    Without ever stopping,
Delivering cards for the Ball,
Invitations to each and to all,
    And he's taken great care
    To plan and prepare
Good things for the Feast, so that every guest
May have for a treat the food he likes best —
Nuts for Squirrels and Worms for Moles,
And little titbits for Beetles and Voles.

Happy-Go-Lucky Grasshopper,
What awful risks he takes!
As Grasshoppers have no brakes
    He doesn't always land
    Exactly where he planned,
To be happy and hoppy and free
Is every Grasshopper's wish —
Happy-Go-Lucky, STOP! or you'll be
A snack for a big-mouth Fish!

    SAFE! He straightens his wig
    And breathes a sigh of relief;
    The shock was almost too big
    For the boatman on his leaf,
But Grasshopper's not afraid in the least
And with hugest hops goes off to the Feast.

Plate 8

WHEN it's dusk or dark on earth,
Dusky, misty, ghostly,
It's then Magician Moth goes flitting mostly,
Softer than a breath.

Marked with a skull since birth
He knows no fear of death,
And when he folds his patterned velvet wings
Keeps very still, as midnight darkens,
Keeps very still, and hearkens
To the faintest, strangest, and most secret things.

They say that whispers from some very far,
Never-seen and nameless star
Give him power to foresee
Happenings unknown to you and me.

Before the Ball was even thought of, he
Knew just when it would be,
So here he is, in the clear light of day,
Famous Magician Moth outside this place of call,
The busy old White Lion,
Buying a jug of honey, something to rely on
Before he flits away
(But not till after sunset) to the Ball.

Plate 9

LOWERS hold for honeybees
Drops of purest nectar,
And Lizzy Bee, of all the bees,
Is the busiest collector.

Humming to herself for hours
Lizzy visits many flowers,
Honeysuckle, thyme, and clover;
Yellow pollen powders over
Lizzy's legs, as round she goes
Probing into every rose —
Lizzy knows, Lizzy knows
Where the sweetest nectar lies.

Oh today a big surprise!
Not a single flower will see
Anything of Lizzy Bee;
Today's her happy holiday
(She deserves one day at least),
She's left the hive to buzz away
With loads of honey for the Feast.

Plate 10

"I WAS saying Good Night to my children,
    Not old enough to have wings
They're still living under the water,
    The greediest, ugliest things;

"In the lake as smooth as a mirror
    I can hardly believe what I see,
While saying Good Night to my children
    I've fallen in love with ME!"

To the Feast and the Ball have now flitted
    Dragonflies red, green and blue,
You can't spend all night at your mirror
    So what are you going to do?

"Me? As I'm a glittering Beauty,
    Though I too was ugly when small,
Of course I must rush off to show off
    My beautiful self at the Ball!"

Plate 11

 ROM their sharp front teeth to the tips of their tails
The Rodents were thrilled by their trip on the rails
In a Midland express with the *Princess of Wales*.

Rat with his hoop,
Shrew with his nose,
Won't leave the fence
Till they see how it goes.

Mad about trains!
Someone must call
And tell them it's time
To start for the Ball.

Going first-class in the Rodents' Express
Mrs Squirrel had managed to put on her dress,
Her butterfly dress — it's a perfect success!

But Rat with his hoop
Shrew with his nose
Can't be bothered
About their clothes.

"No good scolding them,"
Squirrel explains,
"The plain fact is
They're mad about trains."

Plate 12

ALL IN red and yellow
Dressed as Punchinello,
Fox, the crafty fellow,
Travelling to the dance
Casts a wicked glance
Through the carriage door
At the prima donna
On the platform there,
Madame Bella Swanna,
Setting out upon a
European tour.
You may be in danger
From a handsome stranger —
Madame, do beware!
As for Lily Lizard,
Silly Lily Lizard,
Did she know the hazard
Going on her own,
Travelling by train?
"Never be alone
With a man unknown,"
So they'd often told her,
"Specially if handsome:
He might be insane,
Might hold you to ransom."
Fox, he means to hold her.
When he wants his lunch
THEN will come the crunch!

"T'S NO good trying to rush things, is it?"
Said Doctor Vole, making his second visit.
"Tests of your water clearly showed
You'd swallowed some pollution, Toad.
What you now need, as I've already said,
Is to keep snug a day or two in bed.
It's no good fidgeting or cursing.
You're lucky to have splendid nursing
From Cyril Crayfish, your unselfish friend,
And Willy Water-Measurer. You'll soon mend.

"I'm glad they keep your room so nice and damp,
That's very healthy, good against the cramp.
To get you on the way to convalescence
There's nothing like this Anti-Effluent Essence.
There's lots of this pollution now about,
But soon you'll be all right again, and hopping-fit, and out."

Plate 14

Y NAME'S Aranea (Miss Spider to you),
I'm lucky to know, and I'm lovely to view.
As you see, I am rich. The silk which I spin
Is exceedingly strong and incredibly thin.

My maid, Alice Weevil, so faithful and civil,
Has cleverly brought, as I guessed,
My green-and-gold shoes. I *must* look my best,
Very soon now the Ball and the Feast will begin,
And I mustn't be late.

I still have to make up my eyes
(Unlike you I've got eight).
Alice, what is the time? How it flies!

So do I! Through the air, on a gossamer thread,
I shall glide to the Ball. As I float overhead
All will look up, and the dancers will pause
To give me a deafening round of applause.

Alice, good night. Don't lock the front door
Or sit up for me. I'll be back about four.

DREAMY in the afternoon
Froggy went a-wooing, far
Where the clear-cut hilltops are,
Idly touching his guitar,
Noticed Badger drifting by,
Badger in his striped balloon
To the Ball go drifting by,
Not too low and not too high,
Through the dreamy afternoon.

Where the clear-cut hilltops are
Reflected in the glassy lake
Froggy plucked at his guitar
Through the dreamy afternoon,
Ditties drifting on the wind
Fingers picking out the tune,
Never making a mistake.
(Fox was fishing with a friend,
And they listened by the lake.)

Froggy had set out a-wooing
But having sung and having played
And found that there was nothing doing
Comfortably down he laid
Both himself and his guitar,
Where the spotted agarics are.
On that pillow dreaming, he
Saw uprising, circling, see,
Persons known to you and me.

Plate 16

INVITATIONS were sent to the Hornet and Wasp
On condition they laid by their stings.
"They might as well ask us," protested the Wasp,
"To fly to the Ball without wings."

"I hate you," the Hornet replied, "but for once
What you say does seem perfectly true.
I'll never go stingless so long as I live
And if *I* get a chance I'll sting *you*."

"This Ball," said the Wasp, "means nothing to me,
And nothing *you* say means a thing,
So long as I'm airborne, so long as I'm armed,
I shall fight for my freedom to sting."

Those who stick to their principles stick to their stings
And those who have guns will take aim,
But after they've stung, or after they've shot,
What they never will take is the blame.

Plate 17

THERE on the bridge
In the middle of the day
Are several of the guests
Who've come a long way,
The sun's overhead,
The shadows are shorter,
And someone says, "Look!
Who's that by the water?"

"That's Mr Kingfisher,
He's a splendid sight
But looks as if he's waiting
And waiting for a bite,
Unlike us he wasn't
Invited to the Ball."
So just to cheer him up
They give him a loud call.

Mr Blue Kingfisher,
Brightest, bluest bird,
Hears what they're saying
But answers not a word,
And waiting for a bite
He may be there all night.

Let him wait and wish!
If you take a look
You can find a fish
That he'll never hook.
Take a careful look!

PS.   *The fish he won't catch you can easily see*
Outlined up above in the boughs of the tree.

Plate 18

THAT huge new block, in EC4,
Of the Cheddar Bank they built last June
Has a secret flat, on the fourteenth floor,
For Sir Maximus Mouse, the Cheese Tycoon.

There he sits in his cosy room
With a ticker-tape, in view of St Paul's,
To watch how the market rises and falls.
His whiskers twitch at the hint of a boom,
His whiskers droop at the hint of a slump in his
Hundred-and-twenty super-companies.
As a cat will watch a mouse, he stares
At the ups and downs of stocks and shares,
A prince among mice and millionaires.

"Knock, knock," says the grandfather clock,
"Money's not all, money's not all —
He has quite forgotten the Butterfly Ball!"

Plate 19

WITH the setting of the sun
The Ball has now begun
And those who've not arrived must take care,
Must all look out for *that*
Swift and fearsome Bat
Swooping in the twilight – oh, beware!

After sleeping all day long
Upside down, he's feeling strong
But he's hungry, and he's looking for a bite;
As he wasn't asked at all
To either Feast or Ball

He must snap up little insects while in flight;
Because they rightly fear him
They try not to go near him,
And that smartly dressed Cockchafer
Would be a great deal safer
If he'd taken quite a different way tonight.

Plate 20

ROM the castle that towers above the trees
Two he-Ladybirds guarding their flock
Heard a hullaballoo. "Jacky, listen, please,
We don't want our sheep to die of shock,
That noise would give even lions a fright."

Someone was roaring, "Raise the portcullis!
Lower the drawbridge! Here comes the Knight!"
Then out rode Sir Bedivere, whirring along
On his Stag-Beetle steed, and singing a song:

"I'm ready to fight
With Red Ants or White,
With Goblins or Elves;
Myself and my Stag-Beetle,
All by ourselves,
We ride off in quest
Of treasures or dangers,
Monsters or strangers,
A fire-breathing Dragon,
A Damsel distressed —
Adventure, adventure, that's what we need,
Myself and my faithful Stag-Beetle steed!"

Plate 21

WHEN Newts assemble for a drink
They lap up beer and stout and port
 And spirits by the quart,
They'd drink the Atlantic dry, I think,
At least if it were free from salt
 And brewed with hops and malt.

With time to spare before the dance
The Newts all gathered took the chance
By a bright fire – well, what d'you think? –
 To take a little drink:
They thought that it would give them all
 A starter for the Ball.

"Now cheers, my dears," said Mr Newt,
Dressed in his hat and birthday suit,
"We Newts are a good-natured clan,
 Much thirstier than man,
So let's see who can drink the most,
 To him we'll drink a toast."

They laughed, they sang, the fire was hot,
They lurched, and Father took a fall.
Said Mrs Newt, "Do you know what
 You've been and gone and done?
Missed as a Newt, you silly sot,
 Our evening at the Ball!"

Plate 22

THE BUTTERFLIES' AIR-LIFT
AND THE WEEVILS *v.* CATERPILLARS CRICKET MATCH

OW COULD those creatures that slither and crawl
Ever have got to the Butterfly Ball?
All had been asked and wanted to go
But Snails are so sluggish and Slugs are so slow,
    How *could* they have got to the Ball?

"We'll put on an air-lift, I think it our duty,
And ferry them there," said the Camberwell Beauty.
"We'll fly through the sky in this festival weather,
A seven-in-hand all harnessed together,
    And *we* can bring *them* to the Ball."

So Swallowtail, Orange-Tip, Peacock and Brimstone,
Purple Emperor, little Chalk Blue,
Brighter than flags of the quarrelling nations
Happily fluttered and peacefully flew,
    And ferried the Snails to the Ball.

Did they ever look upward, the watchers below?
Not they, nor the fielders, nor those at the wicket;
All were watching to see how this over would go,
And the Weevils' ace batsman, a demon at cricket,
    Was keeping his eye on the ball,
    His weevilish eye on the ball.

Plate 23

THE MOST wonderful tune in the world
(All other claims are false)
Is Simon Centipede's masterpiece,
The Lepidoptera Waltz.

On the night of the Butterfly Ball
We heard the music begin,
Cymbals and harp and drum,
Bassoon, clarinet, violin.

How splendidly Simon plays!
Nothing could be so neat
As the way he strikes the notes
With a dozen or more of his feet.

When the guests began to dance
Even those who had no wings
Flew around, as if in a dream,
On feet like enchanted things.

The dancers went off their heads,
You've never heard such applause
As Simon bowed and bowed
To the storm of "Bravos!" and "Encores!"

When he kissed the Butterfly's hand
And said, "Madam, I wrote it for you!"
Two tears of joy in her eyes
Twinkled like morning dew.

Plate 24

E VERYONE had heard the Feast would be
Spread out under the broad oak tree,
At toadstool tables here are we
Happily eating, as you can see.

The Grasshopper's given us each a treat
By getting us *just* what we like to eat;
On every table there's different food,
Some to be nibbled, some to be chewed.

Moths and Butterflies suck what is sweet,
Squirrels crack nuts, they don't like meat,
Green stuff pleases Hares and Rabbits,
But some of us Insects have cannibal habits.

Caterpillars keep chumbling away
At nice green salads night and day,
But Moles and Frogs like Worms for their tea —
To eat bread-and-butter they'd *never* agree.

What a lot of trouble Grasshoppers take!
There goes one with a strawberry cake,
And Grasshopper, look, this glass is mine,
Please fill it up again with blackberry wine.

Plate 25

SWALLOWTAIL:

"SHELLY SNAIL, that mask you hold
Gives you a look that's young and bold;
What are you really like, I ask,
Behind that brightly painted mask?"

SHELLY SNAIL:

"Swallowtail, the real Me
Behind the painted mask you see
(Truthfully I must reply)
Is someone most extremely shy.
I know this is the one great chance
For me to ask you for a dance
And make your harebell girdle swing
While we perform a Highland Fling,
But oh, you lovely Butterfly,
The fact is, I am much too shy."

SWALLOWTAIL:

"Shelly, I understand you well,
You're only happy, I can tell,
When sitting snug inside your shell.
I shan't forget you while we hop
And flutter in the dance, non-stop,
So when you sit and drink your tea
Inside your shell please think of me."

late 26

T HE BALL is beginning! From every direction
Guests are all crowding to join in the fun;
Was ever there seen such a varied collection
Of beautiful creatures? The Ball has begun!
First the Damsel-Flies' Ballet, so nimble on tiptoe,
With glittering wings, and so famous, these four,
They can kick in a can-can, or dance a calypso,
And whatever they do always gets an encore.

When Rabbit and Fox put on different faces
You can't be quite certain whichever they are,
But soon all the guests will be showing their paces
To the loud hurdy-gurdy and Froggy's guitar,
They'll see Aranea on gossamer prancing
Over Harlequin Hare with his one-hare-band,
And Happy-Go-Lucky Grasshopper dancing
With lovely-winged Butterflies, hand in hand.

With Slugs, Mice, Squirrels, and all sorts of creatures,
Ants, Moths and Earwigs the place will be packed,
Some will say, "*Whose* are those faces and features?"
And all will be happy as act follows act.
Each one will feel that this great Ball is bringing
The joy of a lifetime, and all are agreed
With Froggy, who twangs his guitar, sweetly singing
His favourite song that says *Love's all you need*.

Plate 27

UCH a Ball and such a Feast
 No one can forget:
Oh, if both would last, at least,
One more hour, not finish yet!

Some are sleepy, some could madly
 Dance away till dawn,
Lovely wings are folding sadly,
One small Ant was seen to yawn.

Now the great big Moon is sinking
 And goodbyes are said,
Darkness spreads, and some are thinking,
"Who will light us home to bed?"

Switching on his greenish light,
 Glow-worm's heard to say
(He's so helpful and polite),
"Let me put you on your way.

"With my light I'll guide you all,
 Homeward, like a friend,
While you're sleeping, Feast and Ball
 In your dreams will never end."

Plate 28

ATURE NOTES

GADFLY (Plate 1). Gadflies, also known as horseflies or deerflies, are blood-sucking two-winged flies of the genus *Tabanus*. Gadflies are so called because their bites were supposed to make cattle "gad about" the fields with their tails erect. In fact, this behaviour is now thought to be due to the attacks of a different but equally pestilential species of fly, the warble fly *Haematopota*. There are a number of species of gadflies, and some grow quite large, even up to one inch in length. They are black, brown, or yellow in color, and some types have very brilliantly colored eyes. Gadflies are most often seen during hot weather. They will bite people as well as horses and cattle, and they are often persistent in their attacks.

It is the female gadfly that is the villainess. Males are sedate and rather shy creatures and much prefer a meal of nectar from a wild flower to sucking blood. They spend their time resting on tree trunks, leaves, or flowers or drinking from a pond or stream, while the females home in on to the nearest warm-blooded animal. It is often a case of the biter bit, however, for gadflies themselves are preyed on by dung flies, dragonflies, and wasps.

Tabanid larvae appear to need moist conditions to live in, and eggs are often laid on vegetation overhanging water, into which the tiny larvae fall. They are voracious creatures, capable of disposing of two or three worms, two or three times their own length, within a week.

DORMOUSE (Plate 2). Dormice are rodents that look very much like small squirrels. The ten species of dormice are not found in North America, but are common in Europe, Africa, and parts of Asia. They have soft brownish fur, bushy tails, and small round ears. The dormouse sleeps through the winter, hibernating more fully than most mammals. It owes its name, derived from the French *dormir* (to sleep), to this habit; it also has a folk name, "the sleeper." Hibernating animals are naturally adapted to living through the winter, avoiding a period when food is scarce by becoming torpid and greatly slowing down their metabolism: the temperature of normally warm-blooded animals falls to that of their surroundings. Each autumn dormice fatten themselves up for the winter, and when they waken in spring may weigh little more than half what they did before hibernating.

Dormice live to a great extent in the branches of low trees and shrubs, eating leaves, nuts, and various other kinds of fruit. They are also great nest builders, each individual having a summer sleeping nest in the branches and a winter hibernating nest on the ground. Birds' nest boxes may also be appropriated. The breeding nest is often near the ground.

Like our red squirrel, the dormouse makes itself unpopular by entering houses and careering about in roofs, making a noise that has been likened to that of a herd of small elephants overhead.

MOLE (Plate 3). The mole, an insectivore allied to the shrews, is one of the few mammals that spends almost its whole life underground. Its bodily structure and habits of life are admirably adapted to the excavation of its network of tunnels, some up to a foot beneath the surface, and to hunting its earthworm prey in them: the flexible elongated snout for probing after food, the strong muscular hand-like forefeet for excavation, the cylindrical body for smooth transit. The soft velvety fur, which bends backwards or forwards as the mole moves up and down the tunnel, is also well adapted to its subterranean life.

Moles are proverbially blind, but in fact are not so, although their eyesight is poor. Three other widely held but equally erroneous beliefs about the mole are that it eats its own weight in food every twenty-four hours, that it digs incessantly for food, and that if deprived of food for as little as four hours it will die. In fact, moles eat only about half their body weight in worms each day, get much of their food by picking it up after it has fallen into their tunnels, have three separate eating periods in the day, and can survive for forty-eight hours without food. Though seemingly far from agile, a mole has been seen to catch and kill an animal as active as a frog.

Farmers, gardeners, and home owners dislike moles because of the molehills they throw up in the course of constructing their underground tunnel system. Some molehills are much bigger and contain the mole's nest, but we still know next to nothing about why some moles make these "fortresses" and others apparently do not.

OTTER (Plate 4). The otter is a primarily fish-eating carnivore of the weasel family and, as such, is regarded with suspicion by anglers and fly-fishermen. However, it is probable that otters eat mainly sick or otherwise inefficient fish, and so on the whole do good rather than harm to fish stocks. They are among the shyest of our native mammals, and few people have ever seen one in the wild. Otters grow to be three to four feet in length, have thick, glossy dark brown fur, a long thick tail, and short legs. Their webbed hind feet help to make them agile swimmers. Otters are very playful; they are known to construct chutes in mudbanks and in the snow along streams, where they then slide, one after another, down into the water. Otters breed in holes in riverbanks and appear to do so all year round.

Otters have become quite rare in recent years, partly because they have been trapped for their beautiful and valuable fur and partly because they cannot live close to many people or in rivers or streams that are polluted. The otter looks much like its close relative, the mink, although that animal is smaller and darker than the otter, with a narrower muzzle and a shorter, less stout tail.

RAT (Plates 4, 12). There are two kinds of rats that have been closely associated with man, the black rat and the brown rat, both of which are aliens. The black rat, which—confusingly—can sometimes be brown, has a more pointed snout and a longer, thinner tail; it arrived in Europe in the Middle Ages from the Near East, perhaps in the baggage of returning Crusaders. It was later introduced to America on the ships of early settlers. The brown rat reached Europe about two hundred and fifty years ago and America about fifty years later. It has since driven out the black rat from much of its former territory, except in large towns and seaports. The brown rat is perhaps the most destructive vertebrate pest in the world, and it is regrettable that no really humane way of controlling it has yet been found. It is notorious as a disease carrier.

WEASEL AND STOAT (Plate 4). Weasels are long, thin, short-legged animals, most often seen as they dart across the road in front of an oncoming car. In winter, in the northern parts of the country, weasels lose their reddish-brown color and turn white, although the tail tip remains black. When they have their winter fur, they are known as ermine. Weasels generally hunt alone and usually at night, although they are occasionally seen in the daytime. They are very fast and remarkably strong for their size, and the weasel's slender body allows it to pursue its prey down small burrows. Weasels normally kill and eat smaller animals and birds, but they can handle rabbits and are quite capable of attacking rats twice their size. They often kill their prey with a bite at the base of the skull, but, contrary to many myths, they cannot suck blood from their victims. Weasels should be handled with great care, not only because they can easily twist around to administer a sharp bite, but also because they can leave an unpleasant smell on the clothes of the handler. Other members of the weasel family are mink, martens, otters, fishers, ferrets, wolverines, and skunks.

Stoat is another name for the weasel. This name is often used in Europe and usually refers to the weasel in its brown summer coat. The term ermine is also used in Europe for the weasel in its white winter coat.

HARE (Plate 5). Hares are perhaps best known for being mad in March, a saying that derives from their aggressive courtship behaviour in early spring. Pairs leap freely about the fields, chasing and "boxing" each other. The name rabbit is often inappropriately applied to hares; for example, jack rabbits and snowshoe rabbits are really hares. Hares are born fully furred, with open eyes, and they are able to move around shortly after birth, whereas rabbits are naked and blind at birth. Hares are larger than rabbits and they do not dig or live in burrows, but remain above ground, hiding in vegetation. Hares, like rabbits, are herbivores. In both rabbits and hares, the female is often larger than the male. Like the weasel or ermine and the ptarmigan, hares turn white in the winter, thereby becoming less visible in snowy landscapes. Although mainly open-country animals, hares are not infrequently seen in wooded areas.

BUTTERFLY (Plates 6, 23, 26). Butterflies and moths are members of the same group of insects, the Lepidoptera; butterflies are usually day fliers and moths are usually night fliers. In contrast to the generally more somber-hued moths, butterflies are often very brightly colored. The butterfly goes through four stages in its life: egg, larva or caterpillar, pupa, and adult, and what we call the butterfly is the adult stage. The adult lays eggs, which hatch into small caterpillars that grow as they eat the leafy parts of plants. Some caterpillars will eat only one or two kinds of plants, although others are more general in their tastes. The caterpillar is the stage at which the butterfly is most destructive. Once the caterpillar reaches a certain size, it forms a case around itself, called a chrysalis, and becomes a pupa. During this stage many changes go on within the chrysalis, and the pupa later emerges as a winged butterfly.

Many butterflies have a very unpleasant taste to birds and other predators. They advertise this fact to their would-be consumers with unmistakable patterns and often brilliant colors. If a naïve bird tries to sample such a butterfly, it will quickly reject the unpalatable insect and, having learned its lesson, will be unlikely to sample anything resembling that butterfly again. This is the basis for what is called mimicry, a process in nature in which members of one species resemble members of another species that is unpleasant to taste; thus, members of the first group have a better chance for survival, with less likelihood that they will be eaten. This can result in two different kinds of butterflies which look very much alike. The monarch butterfly—it established the pattern—and the viceroy butterfly, which is the monarch's look-alike, provide a good example of mimicry.

GNAT (Plate 7). Gnats are a family, Culicidae, of two-winged flies, the larger members of which are usually called mosquitoes. Gnats are best known for their biting proclivities on warm summer evenings, when the victims do not much care whether they are being bitten by mosquitoes or gnats, but just reach for the insecticide spray. The black fly, which often makes the north woods unpleasant in summer, is a gnat. Winter gnats, however, do not bite people. These are the gnats that can be seen dancing up and down in small groups as if suspended on strings like tiny puppets, right through the year. They are more conspicuous in winter because there are so few other insects about. Fungus gnats also dance in swarms; their larvae feed on fungi and decaying vegetable matter. One of the most curious gnats is the so-called phantom midge; it has a completely transparent larva, also known as the ghost or glass larva.

GRASSHOPPER (Plate 8). Grasshoppers are related to the tropical locusts, and are distinguished by their overdeveloped hind legs, which enable them to jump considerable distances. Male grasshoppers make a stridulating "song" by rubbing their hind legs against their forewings. Stridulation is also a characteristic of the closely related crickets, which can be distinguished from grasshoppers by their long antennae, among other things. Most grasshoppers have narrow wings that are covered by a pair of flexible wing covers, and strong jaws that allow them to eat tough grasses and other vegetation. Locusts are grasshoppers that, at times, migrate in vast swarms, consuming crops and other plant life in their path and causing much damage.

DEATH'S-HEAD HAWK-MOTH (Plate 9). The death's-head hawk-moth is a large moth whose wing span can reach four to five inches. It has markings that somewhat resemble a skull and crossbones on the back of its thorax. For this reason, and also because it can make a shrill squeak by forcing air from its air sacs through its proboscis, many people regard it with respect. This moth lays its eggs on one particular group of plants, the Solanaceae, which includes potatoes, tomatoes, and nightshade. It is guided to these plants by its acute sense of smell, which is early apparent—the same plants are the favorite diet of the hawk-moth caterpillar. The caterpillar, like most hawk-moth caterpillars, is green and has a horn at the rear end. It is perhaps more frequently seen than the night-flying moth itself.

HONEYBEE (Plate 10). Honeybees are among the most social of all insects, with an elaborate hierarchy of queens, the dominant fertile females, drones, the subordinate males, and workers, the numerous infertile females. Honeybees are not truly domesticated but merely use hives provided by man. They roam freely about the natural environment in search of honey and pollen for food. If the bees in a hive grow too numerous, a group is likely to split off to find a new home. Sometimes these swarms will become feral and nest in hollow trees. Worker bees usually attack and sting humans only in defence of their hives, and queens rarely do even this. They reserve their venom for other queens; but if a virgin queen enters an occupied hive, she will usually be attacked and killed by the workers before she can endanger the reigning queen.

DRAGONFLY (Plate 11). Dragonflies have a fearful reputation in country areas, where they have such names as "horse stingers" and "darning needles." They are, however, quite harmless to human beings, and, for that matter, to horses, as they are unable to bite or sting. This is no consolation for their small insect prey such as midges and mayflies, however, for they are ferocious predators, especially the large kinds known as hawkers and the smaller darters. Even the delicate small dragonflies known as damsel-flies have habits hardly appropriate to damsels. Most dragonflies spend the majority of their time close to fresh water, although some of the larger ones, being strong fliers, may not infrequently be seen well away from it.

In the larval stage, dragonflies are completely aquatic. Their larvae, known as nymphs or naiads, are equally ferocious predators on smaller water creatures. Dragonflies are among the most primitive of insects, having existed for well over two hundred million years. Fossils of giant dragonflies, with a wingspan of twenty-seven inches, have been found in the coal seams of northern France; these are the largest insects ever known to have existed on earth.

SHREW (Plate 12). Shrews are not rodents, like rats and mice, but insectivores, related to the mole. They have much the same tapering snout and soft dark-grey velvety fur as the mole. As the name *insectivore* suggests, they are eaters of insects and other invertebrates, and voracious eaters at that. They are restlessly active little animals, and because of their extremely high rate of metabolism quickly die of starvation if they cannot find a constant supply of food. Even so, they rarely live for much more than a year. It used to be thought that shrews died of shock on being handled, but it is now known that they actually die of starvation through not being fed enough in captivity. There are a number of species of shrews, at least two hundred world-wide. The pygmy shrew is the smallest mammal found in America; it weighs less than a dime.

SQUIRREL (Plate 12). Squirrels are rodents, but of a different family from rats and mice. We all recognize squirrels by their bushy tails and quick, nervous movements. They are very agile climbers and spend most of their time in trees. Squirrels eat berries, nuts, and seeds of all kinds. In the spring, they can often be seen out on the ends of branches eating the new buds. They are, however, truly omnivorous, eating almost anything that they may find. The most common American squirrel is the grey squirrel, which is found in most city parks and is more abundant there than in many more rural and wilder areas. Squirrels live either in hollow trees or in large nests of leaves that they make in the tops of tall trees. Some squirrels, such as the smaller red squirrel, which is plentiful in many wooded areas, occasionally have burrows in the ground. Squirrels do not truly hibernate in the winter, but they are less active in very cold weather, wisely retiring to their nests until it becomes warmer.

FOX (Plate 13). The fox is a wild member of the dog family. Although popularly supposed to subsist on a diet of farmers' chickens, foxes are actually omnivorous, eating almost anything from berries to young rabbits, and from beetles to carrion. The best-known fox, the red fox, ranges in coloration from pale yellowish-red to deep reddish-brown on its back, with a white belly. Other color phases are seen in the silver, black, and cross foxes, which are the same species as the red fox. Red foxes pair, and both partners care for the young. The grey fox is less well known, perhaps because it is largely nocturnal and its fur is less valuable than that of some of the other foxes. The grey fox is more of a vegetarian than its relatives, with fruit and grains forming the bulk of its diet during some parts of the year. These foxes also have the very undoglike habit of climbing trees. Foxes are very attractive animals and have gained a reputation for cunning and intelligence.

FENCE LIZARD (Plate 13). The fence lizard is a small, insectivorous grey or brown lizard that is often seen on wood fences, tree trunks, or tree stumps. If startled when they are on the ground, these lizards will usually run to the nearest tree, climb up it some distance, and then remain quite still. With their coloring, this provides them with some camouflage against the drab wood background. Fence lizards, which are sometimes called swifts, can be found in most parts of the eastern half of the United States, except for the most northern parts.

CRAYFISH (Plate 14, with medicine). The crayfish, crawfish, or crawdad is a freshwater crustacean with large claws, similar in appearance to its near relative, the lobster. There are a number of species of crayfish, each varying considerably in size, but none approaching the size of the lobster. Crayfish are generally found crawling slowly across the bottoms of streams and ponds, where they feed on decaying plant and animal remains. They are also able to propel themselves backwards with amazing speed by flipping their powerful tails. Crayfish are gathered, and often cultivated, for food in Louisiana and some other parts of the country. They are also used for bait by fishermen. Today, crayfish numbers are gradually decreasing, probably because of pollution and destruction of their habitat.

TOAD (Plate 14). Toads owe the worst of their reputation to the fact that they secrete a poison from the warty glands that are scattered over their bodies. They are voracious creatures, eating, according to one nineteenth-century naturalist, "all living animals that are susceptible of being swallowed." They appear to have an almost unlimited appetite. Some of the large toads will even eat mice and small frogs. Toads, like frogs, pass through a tadpole stage, but their eggs are laid in strings, not amorphous masses. As adults, however, toads spend much more of their time on dry land than do frogs. The warty, unattractive appearance of toads has given credence to the faulty notion common in folklore that they also give warts to people.

VOLE (Plate 14). Meadow mice or field mice are really voles. Voles can easily be distinguished from mice by their blunter muzzles and short tails. They are very numerous, normal populations being about three hundred per acre in some areas. They breed throughout the year, having a litter of five or six young as often as thirteen times a year. Their populations tend to run in cycles, sometimes attaining plague proportions. When this happens, large numbers of birds of prey that normally feed on voles are attracted to the area, especially short-eared owls, marsh hawks, and sparrow hawks. Voles are vegetarians and during a plague they may do great damage, not only to grassland but also to saplings, as they kill or deform the young trees by nibbling off the bark.

WATER-MEASURER (Plate 14). Bugs to some people mean all insects, to others just one species, the bed-bug. To entomologists, bugs are all the members of the order

Heteroptera, to which the bed-bug belongs. One of the more specialized members of this same order is the water-measurer or water-gnat *Hydrometra*. It has long legs that enable it to stalk about the edges of ponds and ditches in search of the smaller creatures that form its prey. It is not to be confused with two other kinds of water-bug, the water-skaters *Gerris*, with equally long legs, which glide over the surface of still water, and the water-boatmen *Notonecta*, which propel themselves underwater with their powerful hind legs.

MONEY SPIDER (Plate 15). Money spiders are a family of tiny spiders, the Liniphi-idae, which exist in very large numbers. It has been estimated, for instance, that over a million spiders of various kinds have inhabited a single acre of a grass field in the autumn. These are the spiders whose webs are so conspicuous on dewy autumn mornings, slung between grass stems and on other vegetation and glistening in the early morning sunshine. These webs are sheets or hammocks of silken gossamer. The spiders themselves at this time take off and drift for considerable distances on their gossamer threads. Spiders catch and eat other insects and feed off them by sucking out their body fluids.

FROG (Plate 16). Frogs, like toads and newts, are amphibians, formerly also called batrachians, a class of cold-blooded vertebrates that differ from the reptiles both in having a softer skin and in needing to resort to water to breed. Amphibians also differ from reptiles in passing through a gill-breathing tadpole stage between the egg and the adult animal. Frog's eggs are embedded in a gelatinous cover that is 99.7 per cent composed of water. They are laid in a large sponge-like mass, known as frogspawn. The tadpoles at first consist of little but a head-and-body and a tail. As they gradually develop into frogs, they acquire legs and lungs and lose their tails and the gills that enable them to breathe under water. Frogs hibernate under water, either in the mud at the bottom of ponds or in holes in the bank beneath the surface. Male frogs croak in the spring, usually in chorus, and both sexes grunt. The bullfrog is our largest frog, and it can grow up to six to eight inches in length. Other common frogs are the green frog, the leopard frog, the pickerel frog, and the wood frog. The wood frog, one of the smaller frogs, has dark markings that form a mask extending back from its eyes.

HORNET (Plate 17). Hornets are large wasps. One of the better-known hornets is the white-faced hornet, which builds large round nests suspended from the branches of trees or the eaves of buildings. These nests are made of a paper-like material that the hornets produce by chewing up wood fibers. White-faced hornets have a ferocious sting and their stingers, unlike those of bees, can be used repeatedly. The hornet has a fearsome reputation, as the phase "stirring up a hornets' nest" indicates, but in fact it does not attack man unless provoked. Of course, if you poke at a hornets' nest, you are asking for trouble.

WASP (Plate 17). Entomologists recognize enormous numbers of wasps as members of the order Hymenoptera, to which bees and ants also belong. Wasps are highly social insects, living in communities similar to but less complex than the honeybee community. Most of us are familiar with the paper wasp, which builds multi-cellular nests of a paper-like material under the eaves of garages and houses. The nests are much like those of the white-faced hornet, but they are not covered with a globe-like shell of the same papery material as are those of the hornet. One wasp that is often seen is the blue-black mud-dauber, a solitary wasp that builds a nest of mud in which it lays its eggs. It then fills the nest with its paralyzed prey, which then become food for the larvae that hatch out in the nest. Actually, despite their superficial nuisance value, wasps are useful to man, as they feed largely on flies and other less desirable insects.

KINGFISHER (Plate 18). The kingfisher is one of the most strikingly coloured birds and belongs to a widespread family found mainly in the tropics. It fishes by perching on a branch overhanging the water and plunging in when it sees a minnow or other small fish. It also takes crayfish and other larger aquatic invertebrates. Sometimes the kingfisher will hover and then dive down like a miniature gannet. When it catches a fish, it beats it on a branch or rock to stun it and stop it from wriggling, and then swallows it whole, head first. The belted kingfisher, which is mainly blue and white, is seen in most parts of North America. The smaller green kingfisher, which is mostly green and orange, is found only in Texas, Arizona, and south into Mexico.

MOUSE (Plate 19). Mice, like rats and squirrels, are rodents and are primarily vegetarians, although they will also eat a good deal of animal food when they come across it. The house mouse, which, like the rat, lives closely with man, is thought to have originated in central Asia and to have followed man to nearly every part of the world. The field mouse is really a vole; it has a short tail and makes half-submerged nests of grass in fields and meadows. The white-footed or deer mouse is found in wooded areas. It has a long tail and large ears. White-footed mice are among the few rodents that live together in pairs, jointly building nests of shredded plant material. The meadow jumping mouse has a tail nearly twice its body length. These mice are brown on top and white underneath, and they have very long hind legs. When disturbed, they can make jumps of up to twelve feet in length.

COCKCHAFER (Plate 20). The cockchafer or June bug is a large bumbling beetle that makes a humming sound on spring evenings. Both the adult and the larva are exceedingly destructive insects. A swarm of adult June bugs can strip the leaves off a tree in twenty-four hours. They feed mainly at night and are hidden during the day. Each female lays about seventy eggs. The resulting larvae, known to farmers as white grubs, live for nearly four years underground, feeding on the roots of crops, herbaceous plants, trees, and shrubs. Crows may take a certain amount of grain, but this is more than made up for by the good they do in keeping down wireworms (the larvae of the daddy-long-legs or crane fly) and cockchafer grubs.

LONG-EARED BAT (Plate 20). Bats are the only true flying mammals. Their wings are made up of a thin membrane stretched over elongated fingers. Bats are found almost everywhere, except in the arctic regions. The bats with which most of us are familiar are insectivorous, feeding largely on insects caught in flight. In the tropical areas of the world, there is another group of bats that eat mainly fruit. In the temperate climates, when flying insects are scarce in the colder months, bats either hibernate or migrate to warmer areas. Bats are useful to man as they eat large quantities of insects, but close contact with them should be avoided as they are known to carry rabies, which they can transmit to man and other animals. The cries of bats are so high-pitched that many people cannot hear them. The echoes of these cries are used by bats as a form of natural sonar to locate their prey. Despite the old saying "blind as a bat," bats can see.

ANT (Plate 21). Ants are highly organized social insects of the family Formicidae in the order Hymenoptera, to which bees and wasps also belong. There are about twenty-five hundred different kinds of ants world-wide. Most species live in underground nests, but some make large anthills that stick up out of the ground. These are mostly found in grassy places. Ants are divided into fertile males and females, which are winged, and infertile females, which are unwinged and called workers. There is a mass emergence of winged ants in late summer when the fertile pairs first mate and then tear off their own wings. The so-called ants' eggs fed to fish are not eggs but cocoons in which the grubs or larvae are transformed into adults. Ants have many strange habits. Some farm and milk aphides for their honeydew. Others grow fungi in underground farms. Some capture cocoons from smaller ants' nests and use the resultant workers as "slaves," and still others live in other ants' nests and steal their food.

LADYBIRD (Plate 21). Ladybirds, or ladybugs, are small beetles of the family Coccinellidae, usually red or yellow in colour and spotted black. There are many species of ladybugs, which vary primarily in the number of black spots they carry on their wing-cases. The number of spots can vary from as few as two to as many as twenty-four.

The best-known fact about ladybirds is that their larvae eat plant bugs, especially aphides and scale insects, and so should be encouraged in the garden—the use of DDT sprays, of course, being a notable discouragement as it kills the useful insect as well as the pest. A ladybird lives for about three weeks as a larva, during which time it may eat several hundred aphides. This is followed by a pupal state of about one week, after which it emerges as an adult. The whole cycle, from egg-laying to adult hatching, takes from four to seven weeks.

Ladybirds have a curious habit of assembling in large numbers, often on a post or fence. This is probably because they are unpleasant to the taste, as indicated by their bright warning coloration, and a large splash of their colour warns predators off more effectively.

STAG BEETLE (Plate 21). The stag beetle is a large, dark, ferocious-looking insect with large mandibles in the form of a giant pincer. These mandibles resemble the antlers of the male deer or stag, hence the name *stag beetle*. In spite of their ferocious appearance, these beetles do not attack people, but, of course, a finger placed between their mandibles may get nipped. There are a number of species of stag beetles, in some of which the males have much larger and more elaborate mandibles than the females.

The larvae of the stag beetle are large white grubs with crescent-shaped bodies and rufous heads. The adult female stag beetle lays her eggs in decaying wood, which the larvae spend their lives masticating. Wood is a very difficult material for most animals to digest, and the stag beetle larvae are aided in this by fungi that live inside the larvae in large pouches called fermentation chambers.

NEWT (Plate 22). Newts are amphibians, like frogs, toads, and salamanders, which means that they pass through a tadpole stage. Newts are long, thin animals with very small legs. They look much like salamanders. They are more aquatic than salamanders, however, with some species transforming from the tadpole stage directly, retaining external gills and never leaving the water. Others, like the red-spotted newt, pass through a land stage that is called the red-eft stage. The tadpoles change to efts, which live on land for a few years. Often after a rain these beautiful bright red-orange efts can be clearly seen along the forest floor. The efts eventually return to the water and change into the aquatic adults. Newts tend to lay their eggs on the leaves of aquatic plants. The adult newts feed on small aquatic invertebrates; the tadpole live on algae.

CENTIPEDE (Plate 24). Centipedes are myriapods, a class of invertebrates of equal status to the insects, both groups being members of the arthropods. They live under stones, logs, dead leaves and similar debris, and feed mainly on smaller invertebrates. Centipede means "hundred legs," but different species of centipedes have varying numbers of legs; most have between 15 and 101 pairs. Their first appendages are modified so that they can inject poison into their prey. Centipedes are most active at night and are able to move around very rapidly.

MUSK BEETLE (Plate 24, playing violin) is a handsome green longhorn beetle, with red spots on the elytra (wing-cases), and antennae that in the male are one and a half times as long as the body. It may, however, vary in colour from coppery red to bright blue. Its name derives from the strong musky smell emitted by both sexes. The larvae live in the wood of old rotten willows and poplars, and consequently the beetles are usually found near these trees—and it is from salicin, a bitter substance found in poplars and willows, that the musk beetle derives its distinctive smell. The musk beetle is one of the most widespread beetles and is usually to be seen in July and August.

THE GUESTS' EATING-HABITS (Plate 25). Animals must of necessity eat either animal or vegetable food, because minerals provide little or no actual nourishment. All animals appear basically to need proteins, carbohydrates, mineral salts, vitamins and water. There is a distinction between the vegetarians (top right-hand table), such as the rabbit, hare, vole, mouse, rat and squirrel, all rodents in the broad sense, and the flesh-eaters (top left-hand table), such as mole, hedgehog, shrew, frog, and weasel. But many flesh-eaters, such as fox and badger, are in fact omnivorous, taking animal or vegetable food indiscriminately as they find it. Insects, of course, have quite different methods of eating from the vertebrates, and are in turn divisible into vegetarians, flesh-eaters, and omnivores. Most insects (centre table) have mouth-parts designed to bite or chew, but do not have teeth like mammals. Some insects, however, use a siphoning apparatus, and others have developed techniques of lapping up their food. A distinctive insect method of feeding is the use of a piercing device to reach the food supply, coupled with a means of sucking it up, comparable to the use of a straw to drink liquids (bottom table).

SNAIL (Plate 26). Snails, together with slugs, are gastropod mollusks, mostly of the order Pulmonata, breathing through lungs, not gills. They secrete a mucus, which they lay on the ground before them to form a track on which they walk with their single creeping foot. This mucus hardens, so that the snail leaves a trail behind it. Snails have spiraled shells into which they can draw their bodies. There are many thousands of species of snails, and they are found living in fresh and salt water and on land. Many snails are omnivorous and eat nearly anything in their path, while others are highly specialized in their food habits. Some snails are even predatory and prey on other snails and shellfish. Still other snails are exclusively vegetarian, and this type is often used in aquariums to eat algae off the glass, thus keeping it clean. In some parts of the world various kinds of land snails are raised for food.

FIREFLY (Plate 28). Fireflies or lightning bugs are not flies but nocturnal beetles. Their light is produced by the oxidation of a compound called luciferin and its reflection by means of minute urate crystals. Fireflies are thus luminous (not phosphorescent, which means light produced by previously absorbed radiations). The adult fireflies have a very short life span: they do not feed; they mate, lay their eggs in wet ground, and then die. The larvae eat snails and earthworms and, after several years, finally pupate into adults. Fireflies usually inhabit grassy places, but are much less common nowadays than they used to be, perhaps because of the large amount of insecticide residues now found in the environment.

ANSWER to Dandy Rat and the Footpads Puzzle
In the trunks of the trees, if you stand on your head,
His name (which is Max) can clearly be read.